D0229774

SPOOKY RHYMES!

A Book of 'Orrible Poems and Beastly Verse

BY WILLIS HALL

Illustrated by
ROWAN BARNES-MURPHY

HAMLYN

Published 1987 by
The Hamlyn Publishing Group Limited
Bridge House, 69 London Road, Twickenham, Middlesex, England

ISBN 0 600 53156 2

Printed in Hong Kong by Mandarin Offset

1437

CONTENTS

A Taste of His Own Medicine

In the deepest, darkest dungeon,
Stands the wicked dungeon-master,
With his whips and racks and iron-boots,
Having suffered a disaster.

For at dead of night, by candle-light,
Hell-bent on cruel torture,
He'd grabbed a quaking prisoner,
Snarling: "Come 'ere, lad, I've caught yer!"

Then snatching up his thumbscrew,
The dungeon-master cried:
"Take that, you oafish little brat!"
But his own eyes opened wide.

And "*Ouch!*" he roared,
And "*Oooh!*" he yelled,
As the thumbscrew he applied it,
For in the dark he'd missed his mark,
And his own thumb was inside it.

The moral to this little tale,
Is simple, plain and certain,
Do unto others as yourself,
Or it might be you what's hurtin'.

Believing

I don't believe in vampires,
I'll say it loud and clear,
I don't believe in werewolves,
When other folk are near.

I certainly don't believe in ghosts,
All those that do are fools,
And I know for an absolute positive fact,
There are no such things as ghouls.

So why, when it is late at night,
After all that I've just said,
Do vampires, werewolves, ghosts and ghouls
All gather underneath my bed?

The truth, of course, is obvious,
And plain for all to see,
For though I don't believe in *them*,
They all believe in *me!*

The Monster

Frankenstein once built a monster,
From things that Igor carried in:
Legs and arms, a heart and liver,
Teeth and toenails, bits of skin.

He stitched these pieces all together,
Neatly sewed with cobbler's twine,
Smiled and said to his creation,
"I made you monster, now you're mine!"

He went to see a soccer match,
With his giant, brainless man,
"What a triumph!" said the doctor,
"I've made a football hooligan!"

The Nick of Time

Here's the Phantom of the Opera,
In top hat, cloak and mask,
Sitting in the theatre roof,
Engaged at a dreadful task.

He's sawing at the chandelier,
As hard as he can go,
Hopes to send it crashing downwards,
On the people there below.

At last the ton of crystal falls –
But see the Phantom's histrionics,
For the audience are in the bar,
Swigging down their gin-and-tonics.

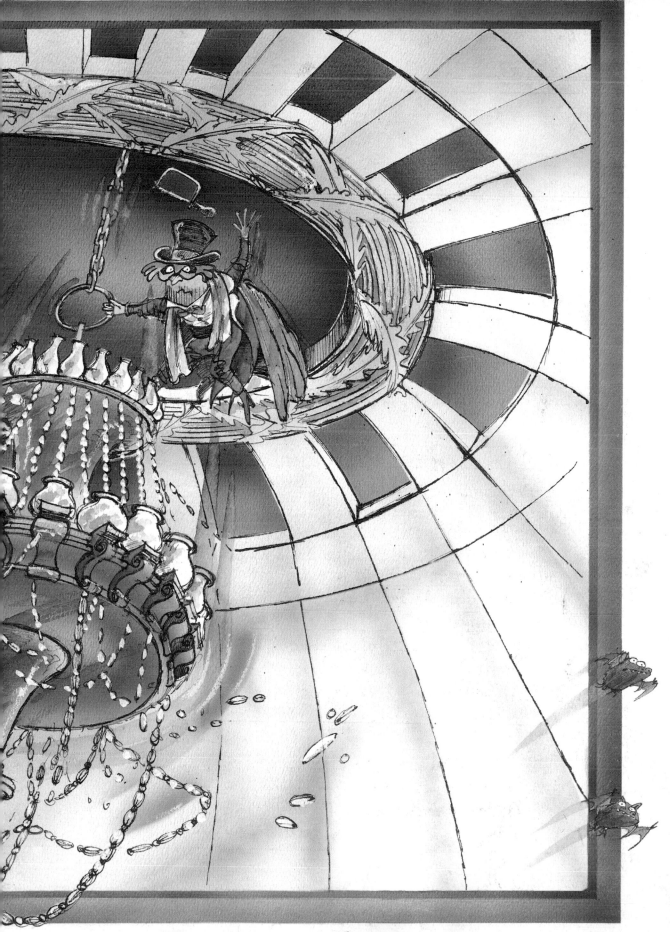

Common-sense

Frankenstein made a monster,
But if he had used his brains,
Instead of harnessing lightning,
He'd have plugged it into the mains.

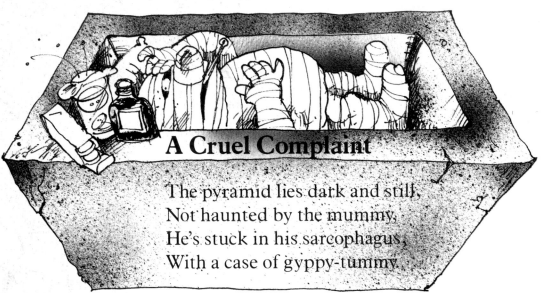

A Cruel Complaint

The pyramid lies dark and still,
Not haunted by the mummy,
He's stuck in his sarcophagus,
With a case of gyppy-tummy.

Quasimodo

"The Hunch-back?"
        said Esmeralda,
"Yes, I know the man
            quite well.
His name
    is hard to remember,
But his face
        sure rings a bell!"

A Practical Solution

"Although I may be quite hirsute,"
Said the werewolf, "I don't give a hoot!
I'll shave off my beard,
And have myself sheared,
Then get it made up as a suit."

Medical Matters

Doctor Jekyll mixed a mixture,
That turned him into Mister Hyde,
Made him go all weird and hairy,
"Save us from him!" people cried.

Every time I'm given medicine
By old hopeless Doctor Lee,
All it does is just taste awful,
I wish Doc Jekyll was our G.P.!

The Haunted Launderette

I met a man in a launderette,
With a beard and long white hair,
He was spinning a sheet in a tumble-dryer,
And nobody else was there.

It was cold and dark in that launderette,
There was rain outside in the street,
And never a word did the old man speak,
As he watched his whirling sheet.

When the sheet was dry he took it out,
Then he draped it over his head,
And peering out was his sad, pale face,
But still never a word he said.

"Are you a ghost?" I put to him,
The old man stroked his beard.
"I don't believe in ghosts," he said,
And promptly disappeared!

Fame

The strangest thing I ever heard,
Once happened to Uncle Bert,
He was bitten by a werewolf,
But said it didn't hurt.

He didn't go to the hospital,
Or call and see the doctor,
He didn't even tell his wife,
In case it might have shocked her.

But when one night the moon was full,
His body went all hairy,
His mouth was full of pointed fangs,
It frightened Auntie Mary.

He *had* to see the doctor then,
Who peered right down his gullet,
"The only certain cure," he said,
"Is death from a silver bullet."

"You can't do that to Bert," Aunt cried,
On that she was emphatic,
Now every time the full moon's out,
She locks him in the attic.

And people come from *miles* around,
To see my Uncle Bertie,
They block the access off with cars,
Which makes the neighbours shirty.

I may not be much good at school,
They say I'm an ignoramus,
But I'm the only kid in all our class,
With an uncle who is famous!

Cousin Dick

My cousin Dick's a skeleton,
He thinks it's rather neat,
He doesn't have to cut his nails,
Or bathe his dirty feet.
He doesn't have to clean his shoes,
Or eat a Brussels sprout,
And strangers scream and run away,
When cousin Dick's about.

My cousin Dick's a skeleton,
I think it's really Ace,
How he can go for days and days,
And never wash his face.
The only thing that bugs him,
I mean what really gets him going,
Is he can't drink Coke or Pepsi,
'Cos his bones start overflowing.

An Unfortunate Odour

Here's the Phantom of the Opera,
In top-hat, mask and cloak,
Enjoying a drink in the theatre-bar,
Like any normal bloke.

He's hoping that the opera-goers,
Won't know that he's the Phantom,
And also that his wit and charm,
Will fool them and enchant 'em.

But "What's that pong?" a duchess cries,
"That niffs like old manure?"
Which serves the Phantom right, of course,
For living down a sewer.

The Stingy Spirit

I met the man from the launderette,
On the top deck of a bus,
"Tell me if you're a ghost," I said,
"And I promise not to fuss."

The old man rattled as he stirred,
For his sheet was covered in chain,
And he fixed me with a frosty gaze,
Saying "I won't tell you again!"

"There are no such things as ghosts," he snapped,
"I've told you that before."
But even as the old man spoke,
He disappeared once more.

Yes, gone in a flash was that strange old man,
At the time I wondered why.
Was it because I'd questioned him?
Should it teach me not to pry?

Then suddenly I understood:
The conductor's foot on the stair,
Convinced me that I'd met Marley's ghost,
Too mean to pay his fare.

All Aboard

"He's rung his last bell," mourners cried,
When their bus-conductor friend died,
Then the coffin-lid groaned,
And a voice inside moaned:
"There's room for two standing inside!"

Tit for Tat

High above the roofs of Paris,
The Hunchback Quasimodo dwells,
Serenading Esmeralda,
Amid the pealing of the bells.

The Paris pigeons cannot stand it,
Ring-a-ding-dong all day long,
Swooping low they aim their droppings.
"Alors!" cries Esmé, "What a pong!"

Question

When he looks in a mirror,
Or so it's said,
A Vampire sees nothing there,
But if there is truth in this rumour,
How does Dracula comb his hair?

Celebration

I don't like weddings, not at all,
I find them just a bore,
At least, that's how it's always seemed,
When I've been to them before.
There's all those *boring* relatives,
That come from far and near,
Scoffing little triangular sandwiches,
And swigging wine and pints of beer,
Saying, "Don't the bridesmaids all look sweet?"
And, "Isn't it a pity,
That the best man's wearing two odd socks?"
Or "Was ever a bride so pretty?"
But I can't wait for Saturday,
To see Aunt Beryl's face,
'Cos cousin Cheryl's marrying,
A Thing from Outer Space!

A Curious Sight

The strangest thing I ever saw,
I'll always remember it too,
Was a werewolf in the barber's shop,
Taking its turn in the queue.

"What are you doing here?" I asked,
"Oh, please will you tell me do!"
"I'm here for a haircut, of course," it snapped,
"And a shave and perhaps a shampoo."

But as morning's dark turned into day,
"Goodness me!" the werewolf said.
There was not one whisker on its chin,
And hardly a hair on its head.

For as all werewolves are wont to do,
It had turned back into a man,
And when the barber cried "Next, please!"
The werewolf got up and ran.

I've often been back to that barber's shop,
Just to peer in through the door.
But I've not seen that werewolf ever again,
And I don't think I will, what's more.

The Phantom Foiled

See the Phantom of the Opera,
As he gazes hard and long,
At the ladies of the chorus,
With their voices raised in song.

He has eyes for fair Brunhilda,
Whom he plans to steal away,
Take her down beneath the sewers,
Where he'll guard her night and day.

Now his evil plan's in action,
Cries the Phantom: "This is it!"
But he misses her completely,

And falls

headlong

into the

pit.

The Horror Film

They let me stop up late last night,
To watch a T.V. thriller,
With Dracula and Frankenstein,
It really was a chiller!
There were vampire bats,
There were evil ghouls,
There were monsters by the score,
There were sharp-fanged rats,
There was blood in pools,
There were murderers galore!
There were these corpses everywhere,
There were even graveyards in it,
And as for creaking coffin-lids,
There was one of them a minute.

But it didn't cause a single fright,
Or give me any fears,
'Cos I watched it with my eyes shut tight,
And both hands over my ears.

A Monstrous Problem

Said the monster deep down in Loch Ness,
"How I long for a change of address,
Without this pollution,
And constant confusion,
From the tourists who make such a mess!"

More Cousin Dick

My cousin Dick (as I've said before),
Is a skeleton by profession,
He likes his simple haunting life,
Never suffers from depression.

Well – one or two things get him down,
(Remember how drinks are a battle?),
And he can't ride his bike down a cobbled street,
Or people complain of the rattle.

There's something else that gets his goat,
(I really don't know why they try it!),
Fat ladies will stop him in the street,
And ask to borrow his diet.

Downside-up

A vampire bat,
Of great renown,
Was known the world over,
To hang up and not down.

At blood-drinking orgies,
Where bats came to sup,
They marvelled at him who,
Hung not down but up.

In every church belfry,
In village and town,
Bats feted their fellow,
Who hung up and not down.

Crying "Raise high your glasses,
And drain every cup,
Here's health to the bat,
That hangs not down but up!"

The Murders of the Wax Museum

There once was a cunning and crazy man,
Who thought of an awful murderous plan,
Dipped bodies in wax so no-one could see 'em,
And put them on show in his Waxwork Museum.

But he did not escape from retribution,
For fire engulfed that institution,
In no time at all his Waxwork Museum,
Became a blazing mausoleum.

The fiery flames burned higher and higher,
With madman and models consumed by the fire,
For no-one arrived in time to free 'em,
And so ends the tale of the Waxwork Museum.

Achievement

We went to New York on vacation,
And then, to enjoy the view,
I was taken up the Empire State,
Which is on Fifth Avenue.
It was great to go where King Kong has gone,
Even though I felt a bit miffed,
For he clambered up the outside,
While Dad made me take the lift.
Yes, I have done what King Kong has done,
But with envy I was green,
'Cos he went up by monster-power,
While I went up by machine.
Oh, I have been where King Kong has been,
Yet his conquest was the greater,
For he climbed the storeys, one by one,
And I took the elevator.

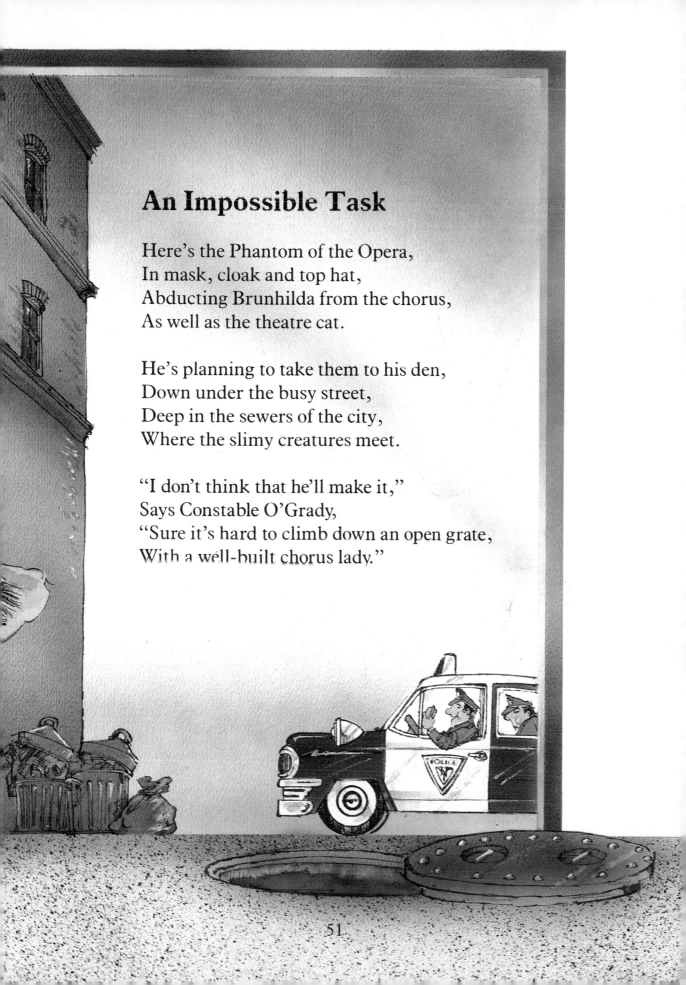

An Impossible Task

Here's the Phantom of the Opera,
In mask, cloak and top hat,
Abducting Brunhilda from the chorus,
As well as the theatre cat.

He's planning to take them to his den,
Down under the busy street,
Deep in the sewers of the city,
Where the slimy creatures meet.

"I don't think that he'll make it,"
Says Constable O'Grady,
"Sure it's hard to climb down an open grate,
With a well-built chorus lady."

Who Done It?

There was an awful pong in school today,
As if something was lying there dead.
Had the Maths Master shot the Games Mistress?
Had the Caretaker strangled the Head?

Had Four-eyes Dart, who takes us for Art,
Stabbed Miss Tench, who teaches us French?
Had Stinker McNabb in the Chemistry Lab,
Been poisoned and died at his bench?

Or could Old Mother Sly, who's in charge of R.I.,
Have encountered some dreadful disaster?
Or was the solution some sort of pollution,
Had destroyed the Biology Master?

For a terrible stink like a mouldering corpse,
Drifted from floor to floor,
As far as the school gymnasium,
Where it crept in under the door.

But we didn't send for Interpol,
Or our local Constable Skinner,
For Tuesday's the day when they boil rotten cabbage,
And serve it up for school dinner.

A Painful Occasion

Said the vicar to Frankenstein's bride:
"This wedding's the first time I've cried.
It's not the bridegroom
That's causing my gloom,
It's the boot to my toe he's applied!"

A Whiskery Problem

A gentleman called Mister Hyde,
Viewed himself in the mirror and cried:
"I hope it won't harm me,
And make me go barmy,
Or even all hairy *inside*!"

The Biter Bit

A vampire out on the spree,
Got what he deserved, believe me,
When he went through a night,
Without getting a bite,
But got bitten himself, by a flea.

The Monster's Lament

Cried Frankenstein's Monster: "By heck!
I feel like a physical wreck!
My face has more stitches,
Than two pairs of britches,
And these bolts are a pain in the neck!"

A Creature of Comfort

In the depths of Dracula's Castle,
In a spooky vaulted cell,
Stands the silk-lined, polished coffin,
Where in daylight he must dwell.

But look, the coffin's empty,
Though the moon has run its span,
For Dracula's bought a real bedstead,
And now comfort is his plan.

Alas, Poor Fred

Uncle Freddie bought a fly-trap,
Took it home and watered it,
Fed it flies and fertiliser,
Watched it growing bit by bit.
Until one day the fly-trap,
Took a shine to Uncle Fred,
Then BITE, MUNCH, CRUNCH,
GULP, SLURP and SWALLOW!
And poor old Uncle Fred was dead.

Cousin Dick Again

My cousin Dick (as I've often said),
Has got no flesh around him,
A skeleton he (alive not dead),
But this does not confound him.

Although he's different from us,
He doesn't seem to mind it,
Dick doesn't moan or groan or fuss,
He takes life as he finds it.

There are some things that make him grouse,
And really get Dick going,
Like being banned from the picture-house,
When a horror-film is showing.

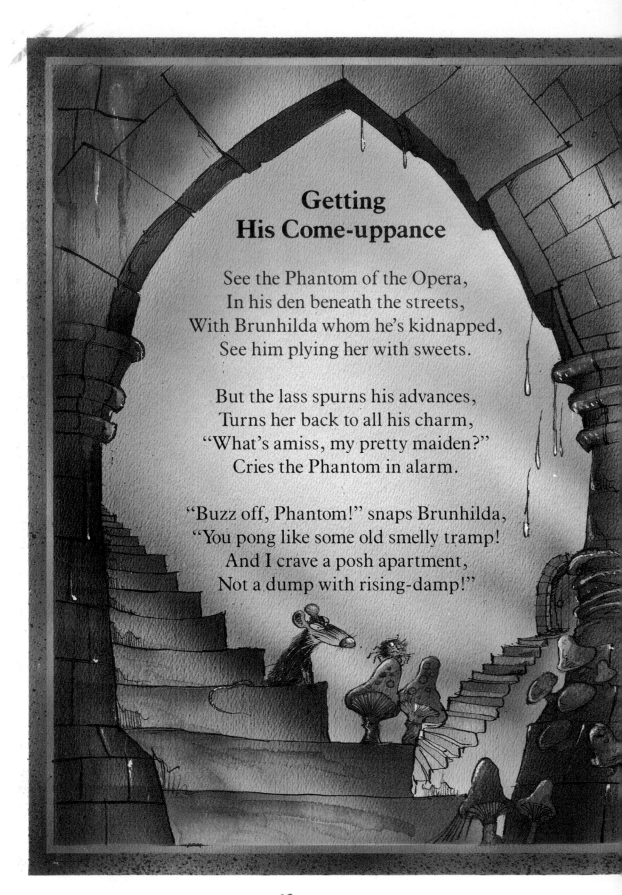

Getting
His Come-uppance

See the Phantom of the Opera,
In his den beneath the streets,
With Brunhilda whom he's kidnapped,
See him plying her with sweets.

But the lass spurns his advances,
Turns her back to all his charm,
"What's amiss, my pretty maiden?"
Cries the Phantom in alarm.

"Buzz off, Phantom!" snaps Brunhilda,
"You pong like some old smelly tramp!
And I crave a posh apartment,
Not a dump with rising-damp!"

A Lucky Escape

A vampire came to our street today,
Biting folks' necks as it went on its way.
It got Edna Stevens and Lionel Brown,
And old Mrs Shuttleworth who lives two doors down.
It got both the Jones kids – that taught 'em a lesson!
And it got everyone in the delicatessen.
But it didn't get me and it didn't get Dad,
And it didn't get Grannie which made us all glad.
It came to our house, but was gone in a minute,
'Cos last night we'd meat-sauce with garlic put in it.

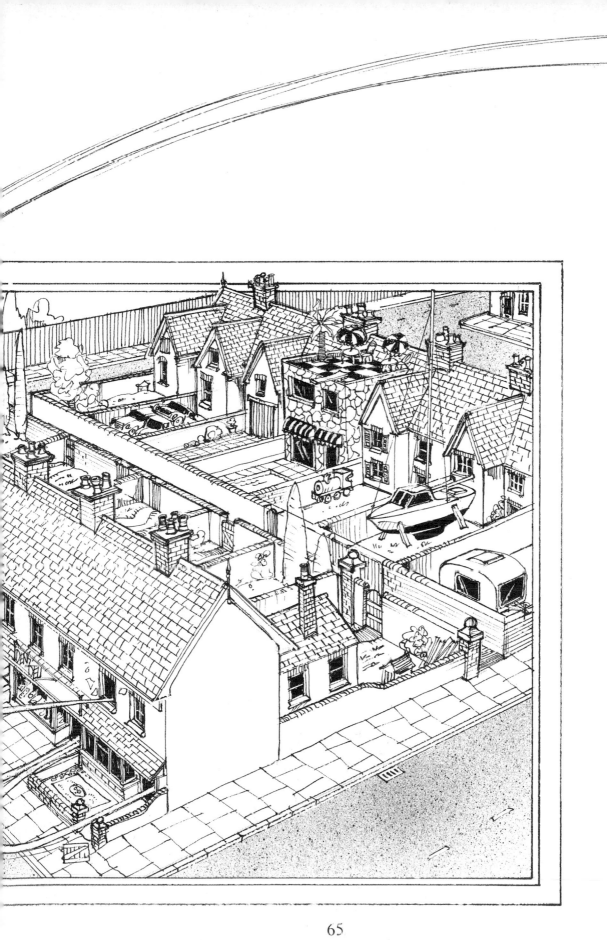

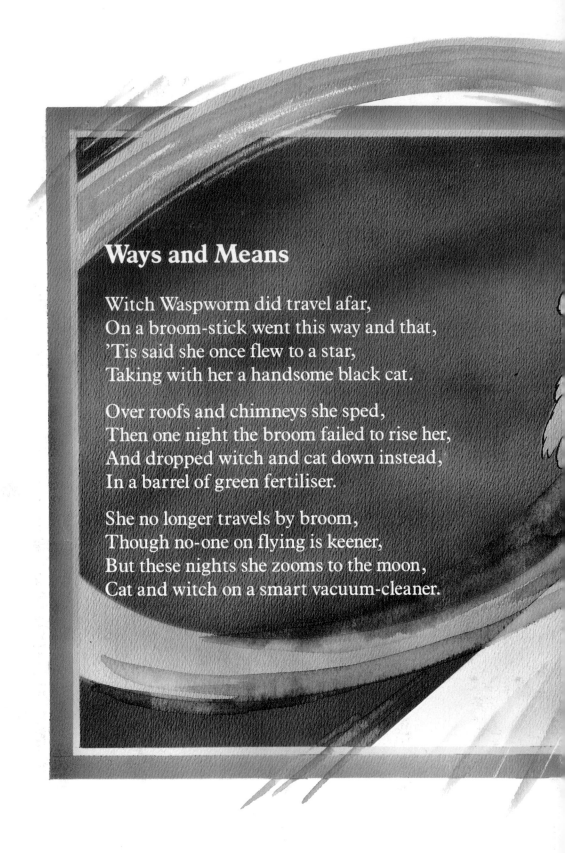

Ways and Means

Witch Waspworm did travel afar,
On a broom-stick went this way and that,
'Tis said she once flew to a star,
Taking with her a handsome black cat.

Over roofs and chimneys she sped,
Then one night the broom failed to rise her,
And dropped witch and cat down instead,
In a barrel of green fertiliser.

She no longer travels by broom,
Though no-one on flying is keener,
But these nights she zooms to the moon,
Cat and witch on a smart vacuum-cleaner.

My Hero

My dad's as brave as a dad can be,
I rate him Number One,
He's not afraid of the dead of night,
Or anything under the sun.

He's not afraid of a late-night film,
Full of horrors on the telly,
And is he afraid of skeletons?
Not dad, not on your Nelly!

He's not afraid of meeting ghosts,
He'd even smile and greet 'em,
And things that scare most dads the most,
My dad could just defeat 'em.

He's not afraid of vampires,
Or a wolf-man come to get him,
If Frankenstein's monster knocked on our door,
He wouldn't let that upset him.

My dad's as brave as a dad can be,
And he's always ready to prove it.
So why, when a spider's in the bath,
Does Mum have to come and remove it?

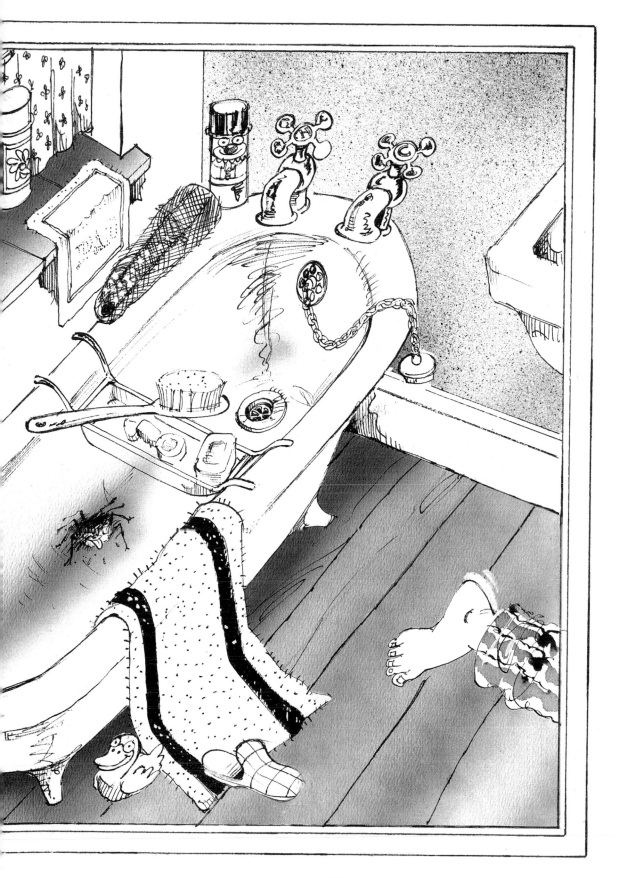

A Candid Opinion

A monster from far distant places,
Cried "What strange looking creatures this race is!
How ugly!" it said,
"To have only one head,
It's as plain as each nose on my faces."

Serves Him Right

Ronnie Rayner put rat poison,
On his mummy's cheese-and-bread,
But his mother wasn't hungry,
Put it in the fridge instead.

That same evening Ronnie's father,
Turned it into cheese-on-toast,
Quite unthinking, Ronnie ate it,
Now he's with the Holy Ghost.

End Piece

See the Phantom of the Opera,
Now Brunhilda is his wife,
She's got him underneath her thumb,
And regulates his life.

She's carpeted the sewer-floor,
And stopped it being smelly,
And where the sewage ran before,
There stands a brand-new telly.

He does not stalk the opera now,
Like the chap on previous pages,
But sells ice-cream to the audience,
And Brunhilda keeps his wages.

A Wasted Climb

Said King Kong: "I think you'll agree,
That bad-tempered it's my right to be,
If I find at the top,
That the souvenir-shop,
Hasn't got any pictures of me."